PUMICE

SCORIA

CONGLOMERATE

FLINT

SHELL FOSSIL

SANDSTONE

ROCKS

AND HOW THEY WERE FORMED

by HERBERT S. ZIM

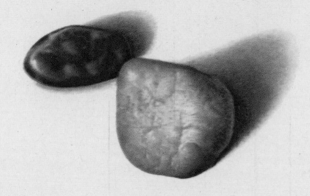

Illustrated by

HARRY McNAUGHT

RAYMOND PERLMAN

ARCH *and* MIRIAM HURFORD

GOLDEN PRESS NEW YORK

Fourth Printing, 1963

Library of Congress Catalog Card Number: 61-5223

ice cap

6,600,000,000,-
000,000,000,000 Tons

The Rocky Ball We Call Our Earth

The earth is a huge, slightly lopsided ball of rock, so enormous that we can scarcely imagine how heavy it is: it weighs about 6,600,000,000,000,000,-000,000 tons. Its diameter through the equator is 7,926.68 miles, but from pole to pole the diameter is 7,899.98 miles, or 26.7 miles less. In spite of this very small flattening, and an even smaller bulge in the southern hemisphere, the earth is still nearly a perfect sphere.

When geologists talk of the earth as a ball of rock, they do not mean it is solidly made up of the stones you see on a rocky beach or on a sheer ocean cliff or in a road cut. Scientists actu-

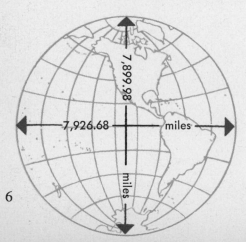

7,899.98

7,926.68   miles

miles

Exact measurements of earth are known.

ally know very little about the rocks deep inside the earth, and even the definition of a rock itself may seem vague and complicated. It is easy to define chemical elements and the minerals they form, but it is not easy to define the rocks of which the earth is made.

All life is, as we know, spread out in a thin layer on, or close to the surface of the rocky earth. Some plants and animals make their homes two or three miles above sea level. Others can survive an equal depth below the surface of the sea. But within this thin six-mile layer, over 99.99 per cent of all plants and animals live, grow, and die.

People are very dependent on the rocks of the earth. Even the first human beings, a million or more years ago, made use of rocks. We are the only animals to use tools, and the first tools were, in all probability, loose sticks and nearby stones. Ancient men discovered that they could hammer with stones, throw them, and even kill animals without endangering themselves. The first tools were stones picked up at random by these early hunters. Later, men learned to chip stones in order to make sharp cutting edges. Still later, stones were polished to produce a finer kind of tool. Before the Stone Age was over, man was well on the way towards what we call civilization, and this was possible partly because of the rocks he had learned to use.

For a million years man used stone tools.

7

30,000 feet

25,000

20,000

15,000

10,000

5,000

Sea Level

5,000

10,000

15,000

20,000

25,000

30,000

Mt. Everest, nearly six miles high, is the earth's highest mountain. A Texas oil well, about five miles deep, is the deepest hole ever dug into the earth.

The story of where rocks come from is closely related to the origin of the earth, and this mystery is yet to be unraveled. The best guess is that the earth and the entire solar system have been in existence for a little over four billion years.

Astronomers get a fairly good idea of the chemical composition of the universe by studying the light from the stars and the sun. But as soon as scientists have to deal with the smaller, colder bodies like the planets and satellites, information is more difficult to obtain. Our direct knowledge of rocks is limited pretty much to the crust of our earth. The deepest hole that man has ever been able to dig in it is a Texas oil well that goes 25,340 feet deep. This is only about five miles down, a mere pinprick into the crust.

Scientists can measure the age of rocks that contain uranium quite accurately. Uranium in a rock slowly but steadily changes to one kind of lead. Thus, careful measurements to find the relative weight of uranium and lead in the rock can be used to measure the rock's age. When about one quarter of the uranium has changed to lead, two billion years have passed. This is almost the age of the oldest known rocks, found in the mountains of India.

8

In recent years, astronomers and geologists have shown that the story of the origin of the world is very complicated. Yet everyone agrees that the earth, the planets and the sun are made of *matter*. Therefore, understanding what is meant by matter is the first step in understanding rocks.

Matter is anything which occupies space, has weight and can be detected by some means or another. Each bit of matter on earth or in the universe attracts all other bits of matter. This ever-present attraction is known as gravity or gravitation.

All matter is made of about 100 different chemical elements. Over 99 per cent of the material in the earth is made of the 30 lightest elements. All our rocks are made of these 30 light elements. If the sun and the other stars are included, the two lightest elements —hydrogen and helium—make up nearly all of the matter in the universe.

On the hot surface of the sun, most atoms (the smallest particles of an element) are independent of each other. On the earth, atoms usually combine to form molecules. Sometimes two or more atoms of the same kind will join together. Atoms of hydrogen and oxygen are usually joined in pairs. More often, two or more different elements unite, forming a molecule made of several kinds of atoms.

The hundred or more kinds of atoms can combine in millions of different ways. In each case a different molecule is formed. Living things contain large, complex molecules. Nearly all of them include atoms of carbon joined with atoms of hydrogen, oxygen, nitrogen, sulfur and phosphorus. In the crust of the earth the 30 or so lightest elements have joined together to make thousands upon thousands of different molecules. These molecules form chemicals which occur naturally in the crust of the earth. When these natural chemicals have a definite crystal shape and are not formed in or by living things, they are then called minerals.

Thousands of kinds of minerals are known, but only a hundred or so are common. These common kinds are made mainly of eight elements—oxygen, silicon, aluminum, iron, calcium,

The Thirty Lightest Elements in the Earth's Crust

Atomic Number		Symbol	Atomic Number		Symbol
1	Hydrogen	H	16	Sulfur	S
2	Helium	He	17	Chlorine	Cl
3	Lithium	Li	18	Argon	A
4	Beryllium	Be	19	Potassium	K
5	Boron	B	20	Calcium	Ca
6	Carbon	C	21	Scandium	Sc
7	Nitrogen	N	22	Titanium	Ti
8	Oxygen	O	23	Vanadium	V
9	Fluorine	F	24	Chromium	Cr
10	Neon	Ne	25	Manganese	Mn
11	Sodium	Na	26	Iron	Fe
12	Magnesium	Mg	27	Cobalt	Co
13	Aluminum	Al	28	Nickel	Ni
14	Silicon	Si	29	Copper	Cu
15	Phosphorus	P	30	Zinc	Zn

QUARTZ

HEMATITE

CUPRITE

SILICATES

LEPIDOLITE

BIOTITE

AUGITE

OLIVINE

SERPENTINE

ORTHOCLASE

Oxides and silicates are the two most important mineral groups. Made of eight elements combined in various ways, they constitute 99 per cent of the earth's crust.

sodium, potassium and magnesium. These eight elements, joined together in various ways, make up nearly 99 per cent of the crust or outer part of the earth.

One important group of minerals in the earth's crust are the oxides. Here, the molecule is made of one or more atoms of oxygen combined with one or more other elements. Best known and most important of all the oxides is silicon dioxide, the chemical name for quartz or sand. Quartz is the most common mineral that is found in the earth's crust.

Another common group of minerals are the silicates. Here silicon and oxygen are once again combined. But in addition, one or more metals such as aluminum, calcium, sodium or potassium are part of the molecule. Silicates are the most important group of rock-forming minerals. Whether in the form of silicon dioxide or in the form of silicates, the two elements silicon and oxygen together make up 83 per cent of the crust of the earth. Six metals make up 16 per cent; other elements add up to a scant one per cent. Iron, our most important metal, is in the less-than-one per cent group; so are all the precious metals. All of these together are the materials of which the earth is made.

10

Ice that covers vast areas in the arctic and antarctic regions is considered a rock.

The Nature of Rocks

To the geologist, rock is the *natural, solid material* that makes up the earth. The first word, "natural," immediately eliminates man-made materials like cement, glass, brick, and steel, even though these all come from the crust of the earth.

The second word, "solid," rules out the air and other gases, the oceans, rivers, lakes, and other liquids. However, solids can be changed to liquids and gases by being heated; liquids and gases can be changed into solids by being cooled. The definition of a rock means solids at temperatures which normally occur in the earth's crust.

Even this does not cover everything, because one of the most common chemical compounds on the surface of the earth may or may not be a rock, depending on its temperature. This chemical compound is water — H_2O. Water makes up nearly three fourths of the surface of the earth. Most of it is in the form of a liquid, and while liquid water affects the rocks of the earth in many ways, water is not a rock. However, in the arctic and antarctic regions, and in the temperate regions during winter, millions upon millions of tons of water are a hard, frozen solid. In the antarctic, ice occurs

11

Hot lava pouring from a volcano is also a rock.

in layers nearly two miles thick. Ice is, therefore, a rock, and geologists study the great ice fields just as they study other rock formations.

In speaking of rocks, geologists use the word "solid" in its technical sense. A solid is matter that is not a liquid or gas. What the geologists would call "solid rock" might seem strange to you.

The wet sands on the beach and the shifting sands in the desert are a solid —and a rock. This is also true of the layers of mud and muck in the swamps, or the ash and cinders from volcanoes. They are rock also.

The third word, "material," brings no additional problems to the definition of a rock. But it may be well to

Sand fits the definition of a rock. So does soil.

A worker lifts asphalt, an organic rock, in a Trinidad asphalt lake.

point out that the materials in the crust of the earth may have two distinct origins. Most of the material in the crust of the earth is inorganic. This means that it is in no way related to life or living things. Lava pouring from a volcano makes an excellent example of inorganic material. So do the great masses of granite pushed miles into the air as part of the Rocky Mountains.

While most rocks are made of materials which are not or never have been alive, some rocks are organic—made by living things. Coal and oil deposits, for example, are the remains of ancient plants. Oil, you might say, is a liquid and therefore is not a rock. However, there are no great underground lakes of oil as some people imagine. The oil is usually soaked up in the pores of sand and other rocks. Under special conditions it will drain into wells where it is pumped to the surface. Millions of gallons of oil are locked up in rocks, especially in the oil shales of Alberta, Canada, and other places. Asphalt is another organic rock. Great deposits of it are found on the island of Trinidad.

Less well-known are the rocks which have formed from the remains of sea animals. Shells cemented together form several kinds of limestone. Sometimes these are shells of microscopic animals; sometimes they are larger shells.

ROCKS OF ORGANIC ORIGIN

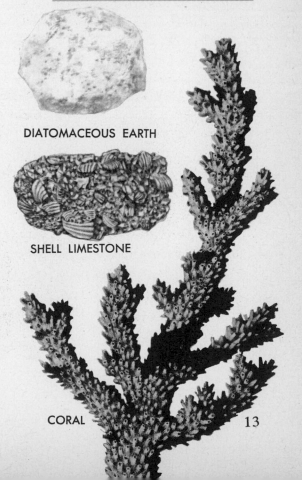

DIATOMACEOUS EARTH

SHELL LIMESTONE

CORAL

13

Coral is another kind of rock made by living things. Coral animals take lime from the sea water and build it into reefs in which millions upon millions of coral animals live. Islands of coral dot the South Pacific. A few microscopic plants and sponges have silica skeletons. Under certain conditions these, too, form organic rocks.

One final explanation, and the definition of rocks is about as complete as it can be. The definition implies that rocks are *large* masses of natural, solid material, big enough to form a distinct part of the earth's crust.

Diamonds are not rocks, even though they are found in the crust of the earth. But if a whole mountain of diamonds was discovered, then it would be correct to call diamonds a rock.

There are places where one can see mountains of marble, quartz, granite or limestone. You can find large beds of coal, shale or lava. These are rocks. There are the many miles of rich soil, more miles of sand in the deserts and on the shores. They all make up major parts of the earth's crust, so they are called rocks.

You may have noticed that the definition of a rock does not say anything about minerals. This is odd, for we commonly think of rocks and minerals as going hand in hand. Most often they do. However, all minerals are inorganic. They are chemical compounds and therefore have a definite chemical composition. Mixtures of minerals often do form enough of the earth's crust to be considered rocks. Granite, made

MEDIUM-GRAINED GRANITE

quartz

feldspar

biotite mica

FINE-GRAINED GRANITE

RED GRANITE

POLISHED RED GRANITE

Granite is a rock which is made up mainly of three minerals.

14

mainly of three minerals—mica, feldspar and quartz, is undoubtedly a rock.

There are also times when a single mineral may form a rock. Quartz is a common mineral. Some forms of sandstone are made up of 99 per cent pure quartz. In this and other cases the rock and the mineral are made of the same chemical. This may also happen in the case of the mineral, calcite, which forms a kind of pure marble. Here again the rock and the mineral are the same. Gypsum is another rock made of a single mineral. The mineral kaolin makes fine clay and forms still another kind of rock.

However, rocks may be of materials which are not minerals at all. Volcanic glass or obsidian is not a mineral but it frequently forms rocks. Coal, peat and asphalt are not minerals but they are rocks.

In spite of the difficulty in defining rocks, most rocks are easily recognized when you see them, and most are made of minerals or mineral-like substances. They are usually solid, hard, and heavy, compared to the other materials you see and use daily.

The study of rocks is petrology. It is a difficult science, for most rocks are harder to identify than birds, flowers or trees. But the study of rocks is important, for rocks and minerals yield the materials that make modern civilization possible. The rock which forms soil is the basis for life on land. Dissolved minerals taken from the rocks

CALCITE

GYPSUM

SANDSTONE

KAOLIN

Sometimes a single mineral such as gypsum, calcite, quartz or kaolin may form a rock.

When sea water evaporates the chemicals in it may form rocks, also.

Composition of solids which make up 3.5 per cent of sea water	
Nonmetals	*Per Cent*
Chlorine	55.0
Bromine	0.2
Sulphates (sulfur and oxygen)	8.0
Carbonates (carbon and oxygen)	0.2
Metals	
Sodium	30.0
Potassium	1.1
Calcium	1.2
Magnesium	4.0
Other (gold, copper, iron, etc.)	0.3
Total	100.0

15

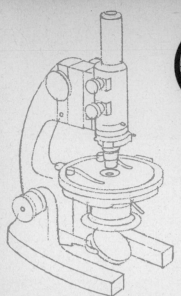

Geologists may identify some rocks by examining them under a microscope, using polarized light, which produces varied light patterns depending upon the particular minerals.

by running water make the sea salty and make ocean life possible to exist.

The identification of rocks is easiest when the rocks are made of minerals and when the minerals are large enough to be identified. When the rock is fine-grained and when the minerals all look alike, as they do in some of the dark rocks, it takes skill to identify them. The geologist will often cut a piece of rock with a diamond saw and polish one surface until it is perfectly smooth. He then cements the smooth surface to a glass slide, and polishes the rest of the rock until it is paper thin. This thin layer of rock is examined under a microscope, using polaroid light. As the light passes through the minerals in the rock, it is altered, producing beautiful colors. These colors depend on the kind of minerals and on the angle at which the crystals have been cut. Such patterns aid in identification.

Identification of rocks involves much more. The texture, color, hardness and relative weight of the rock can also be used as clues. The geologist also looks for the geologic structures in which the rock occurs. Certain rocks are found only in volcanoes, others in caves. Still others are more likely to be found in valleys than on high ridges.

Simple laboratory equipment for identification of minerals

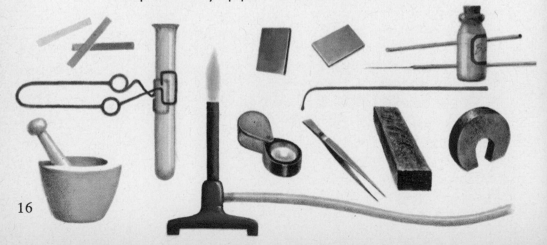

Rock-forming Minerals

Since most rocks contain minerals, some knowledge of minerals is necessary to identify rocks. Because minerals are chemicals, they have special properties which aid in their recognition. Minerals are easily identified by the chemist, by chemical analysis.

One property of minerals which depends on their chemical composition is the specific gravity or relative weight of the mineral. When molecules are packed together with a minimum of waste space, as in the metals, the mineral weighs more. The specific gravity of minerals is compared to water, which has a specific gravity of 1. Common minerals range from 1.7 specific gravity, for borax, to 19.3, for gold.

Most minerals also have a distinct crystal form. This, in turn, depends on the arrangement of the molecules in the mineral. Mineral crystals fall into six systems, and these can be identified by the angles of the crystal. Even a small fragment of a crystal is enough to give a clue to its structure and its crystal form.

The way a mineral breaks in flat planes is called its *cleavage*. This, too, can be used in identification. Mica is an example of perfect cleavage. Minerals also break in an irregular way. This kind of breakage is called *fracture* and it, too, helps identify a mineral.

GALENA   HALITE

ZIRCON   RUTILE

SULFUR   STAUROLITE

EPIDOTE   AUGITE

The form of a crystal is essential in identifying minerals. Shown here are the six crystal systems and examples of minerals found in each.

Left, the Cubic (Isometric) System: the three axes are of equal length and at right angles to each other, as in a cube. Right, the Orthorhombic System: the three axes are all at right angles, but all of different lengths.

Left, the Tetragonal System: two axes are of equal length, and one unequal. All the axes are at right angles to each other. Right, the Monoclinic System: three unequal axes, two not at right angles, the third making a right angle to the plane of the other two.

Left, the Hexagonal System: the three axes are equal and at 120° angles arranged in one plane, with one more axis of a different length at right angles to these. Right, the Triclinic System: three unequal axes, but none forms a right angle with any other.

QUARTZ   CALCITE

AMAZONSTONE   RHODONITE

CLEAVAGE

Cubic cleavage

Basal cleavage

FRACTURE

Conchoidal fracture

Earthy fracture

All minerals have a definite hardness, which is the mineral's ability to scratch or be scratched. Hardness is generally measured on an arbitrary scale of 10. Hardness tests are easy to do. In addition to minerals of known hardness, common substances like a penny (hardness 3), glass (hardness 5.5), and a steel file (hardness 6.5) can be used.

The color of minerals is not important in identification because the color may be due to impurities or surface changes. *Streak* is the color of a powdered mineral, and *luster* is the way the surface of a mineral reflects or breaks up light. Besides these properties, certain minerals respond to ultraviolet light and give off brilliant colors. This fluorescence is also used in identification. Other minerals are magnetic.

Some have electrical properties. These and many other properties of minerals helps identify them in the field and in the laboratory.

The rock-forming minerals are a group of little importance as gems or as sources of metal. But they have great importance in the overall history of the earth. The rock-forming minerals are the ones which make our soil and the land on which we live.

Of all the rock-forming minerals, the simplest and most widespread is the mineral quartz—silicon dioxide. Quartz occurs in many forms, some of them very beautiful. These are used as gems. Ordinary quartz is a colorless, glassy mineral which may form a six-sided crystal. It has a hardness of 7 and a specific gravity of 2.6. It breaks in the same kind of shell-like surface

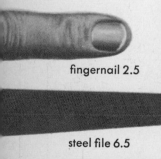
fingernail 2.5

steel file 6.5

knife blade 5.5

window glass 5.5

penny 3

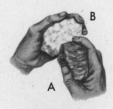
B
A
A scratches B

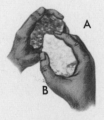
A
B
B does not scratch A

Hardness Table	
1	Talc
2	Gypsum
3	Calcite
4	Fluorite
5	Apatite
6	Orthoclase
7	Quartz
8	Topaz
9	Corundum
10	Diamond

CRYSTAL QUARTZ

ROSE QUARTZ

MILKY QUARTZ

CHALCEDONY

FLINT

JASPER

you find in broken glass. Large crystals of quartz are rare and are valued for their uses in radio and electronics. Crystalline quartz is found in rocks which were once melted, though this kind seldom forms good crystals.

Under certain conditions quartz will dissolve in alkali water and will re-form as a noncrystalline quartz. These forms of quartz are called agate, onyx or chalcedony. Crystalline quartz is the usual rock-forming mineral. Noncrystalline quartz is not.

Gypsum, calcite, dolomite, and halite (rock salt) are occasionally rock-forming minerals too, but, by and large, the rest of the rock-forming minerals are silicate minerals. Probably the most important of the rock-forming

minerals are the feldspars. This is a difficult family of minerals to understand because they grade off one into the other, and are hard to tell apart. All feldspars contain aluminum, silicon and oxygen. They also contain one or two metals such as sodium, calcium and potassium. In a general way, potash or potassium feldspars are put into one group, and soda or sodium feldspars are put with the calcium feldspars into another group.

Not only the amount of feldspar but the kind of feldspar is important in rock identification, especially in the identification of rocks which were once melted. Feldspars have a hardness of about 6. Most are light colored—white, pinkish, orange or pale blue. Feldspar

BLUE CALCITE

GYPSUM

DOLOMITE

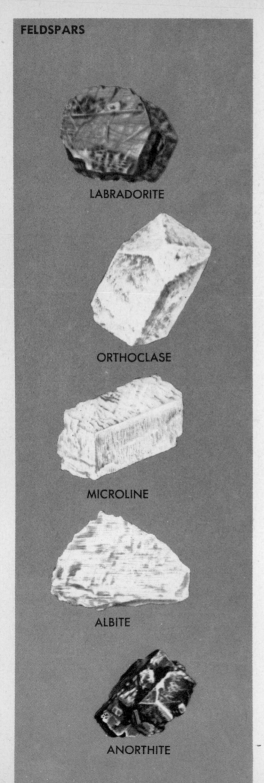

LABRADORITE

ORTHOCLASE

MICROLINE

ALBITE

ANORTHITE

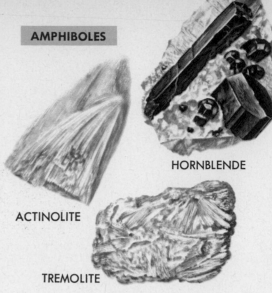

HORNBLENDE

ACTINOLITE

TREMOLITE

is crushed to manufacture glaze and enamel for pottery. When feldspars break down they form clay, another important rock.

Micas are better known than feldspars because the "books" of mica can be peeled into flat, thin sheets. This has made mica useful in electrical insulation. Micas nearly always occur in rocks which have been heated, squeezed or folded. They too are silicate minerals. Some varieties contain iron. In a general way they are made of the same elements as feldspars—silicon and oxygen plus metals such as potassium, sodium, magnesium and lithium.

Many rocks consist of mica or some other dark mineral combined with feldspar and quartz, two light minerals. In addition to mica, the two best known dark minerals are the amphiboles and the pyroxenes. These are also silicates. Hornblende is a common, dark green

20

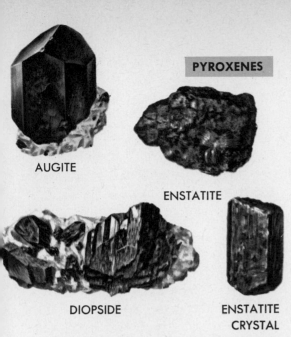

AUGITE

ENSTATITE

DIOPSIDE

ENSTATITE
CRYSTAL

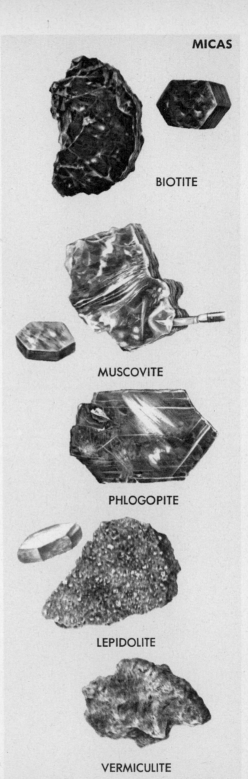

BIOTITE

MUSCOVITE

PHLOGOPITE

LEPIDOLITE

VERMICULITE

amphibole. Augite is a similar-looking pyroxene. Both have the same hardness (5 to 6). They are easily confused but the cleavage angles are a very good way to tell them apart.

Another family of the rock-forming minerals are the zeolites, a group of two dozen minerals which are chemically similar to feldspars. Most zeolites are soft, light minerals. Some have attractive crystal forms.

Garnets, which people often think of as gems, are common enough to be a rock-forming mineral. They too are silicate minerals, usually containing two metals. Garnet crystals often form with 12, 24, 36 or 48 faces. Because garnets are hard (hardness 7) they are used in making "sandpaper."

Other less important rock-forming minerals should at least be mentioned. There is olivine, a green silicate containing magnesium and iron; chlorite,

21

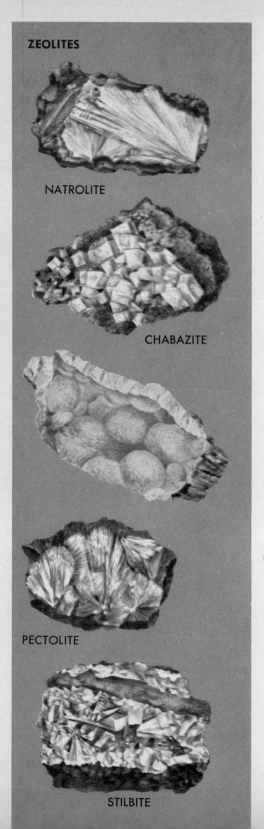

ZEOLITES

NATROLITE

CHABAZITE

PECTOLITE

STILBITE

a darker green mineral; and serpentine, which is mainly magnesium silicate. Talc, from which talcum powder is made, is one form of serpentine.

The way minerals form rocks is a complicated process. It involves chemical reactions at high temperatures and pressures. These different conditions, which may occur within or beneath the crust of the earth, produce a variety of rocks. While these rocks are quite alike chemically, they differ greatly in their physical and mineral characteristics.

All minerals are found in rocks. Diamonds are found only in a volcanic rock called kimberlite. Other minerals, like quartz and calcite, may be found in many different rocks. The chance of finding gold in limestone is practically zero, but the chance of finding it in rocks which were once melted is much greater.

OTHER ROCK-FORMING MINERALS

OLIVINE

ALMANDITE
GARNET

CHLORITE

SERPENTINE

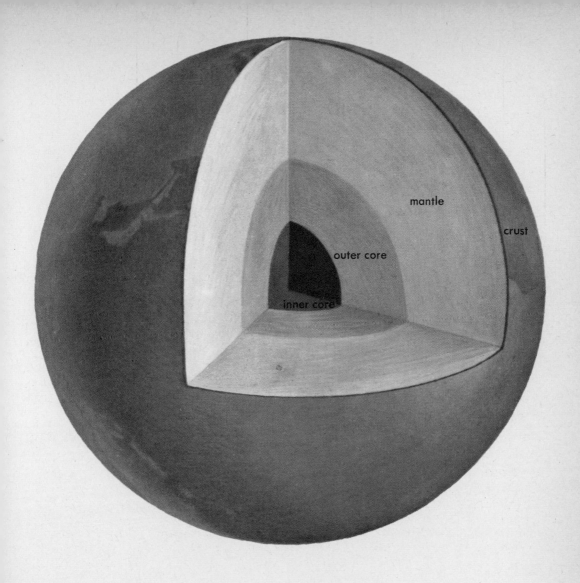

mantle

crust

outer core

inner core

Igneous Rocks

The first large group of rocks—the igneous rocks—are those which were formed from melted or molten materials. The word "igneous" is like the words *ignition* or *ignite*. It refers to fire or heat. Igneous rocks were once magma, a thick, hot liquid deep in the earth. Since all igneous rocks come from inside the earth, let us take a quick look at what is inside.

The deeper we go into the earth the less is known about its structure. There is some knowledge based on earthquake waves, the behavior of the earth as a spinning planet, and on laboratory experiments with rocks under high pressure. These suggest that the very core of the earth is probably iron or iron alloyed with nickel and cobalt. Pressure on the rock near the earth's center may be in the neighborhood of 25,000 tons per square inch. The rock of this rigid inner core—which extends 790 miles out from the center of the earth—is somewhere between 10 and 15 times as dense as water. Surrounding this inner core is another zone some 1,360 miles in thickness. This outer part of the core of the earth also seems to be of dense material, but certain types of earthquake waves do not go through it. Since these earthquake waves travel through solids and not through liquids, it is possible that this outer part of the earth's core acts like a dense liquid. The heavy core of the earth is about 4,300 miles in diameter.

Surrounding the core of the earth is a zone or mantle layer close to 1,800 miles thick. This is a solid, rocky layer which may grade into the iron core. The last 20 or 30 miles out from the center forms what is called the crust of the earth. This is a term left over from the old days when people imagined that the interior of the earth was a great mass of molten rock and searing flames. A thin crust was thought to surround this fiery interior. Every now and then the crust would crack and puncture to let flames and volcanic rock pour forth. Even though this idea about the interior of the earth is false, the term "crust" is still used for the outermost layers of rock.

The crust of the earth contains two distinct types of rocks—forgetting for a moment the soil, sediments, debris,

The earth's crust or outer layer is 20 to 30 miles thick. The continents are supported by a layer of sial. Under the sial, and under the oceans, is the sima, and below that is a zone of glassy rock extending to the upper edge of the earth's mantle.

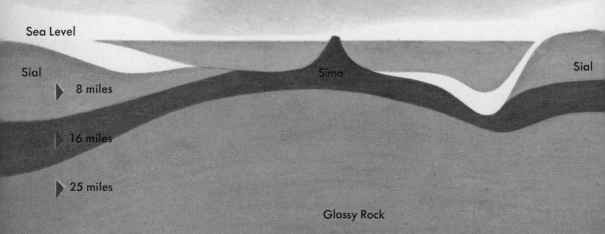

Sea Level

Sial

8 miles

16 miles

25 miles

Sima

Sial

Glassy Rock

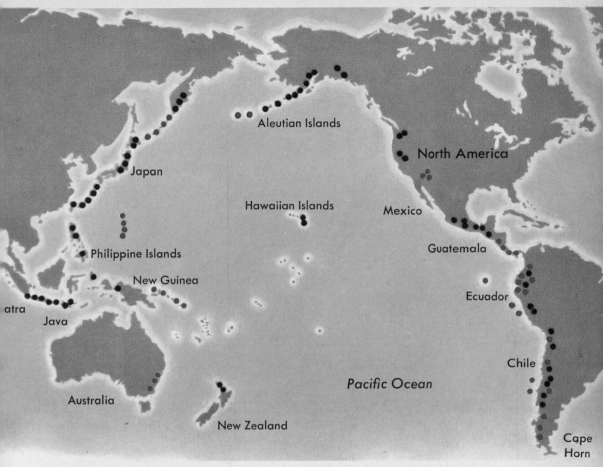

The Pacific Ocean Basin is surrounded by volcanoes, forming "a ring of fire."

water and ice that coat the surface. The continents are supported by the crystalline *sial*. Sial is a word made from the abbreviations for *si*licon and *al*uminum, and it is used because the rocks underlying the continents are rich in these elements combined with oxygen. Sial rocks are light in color and light in weight. They are the rocks that form our great mountain ranges.

Lying underneath the sial and lying directly under the great Pacific Ocean Basin is the *sima*. This word is made from the abbreviations for *si*lica and *ma*gnesium—again because these elements are abundant in the rock. Volcanic lavas are of a silica-magnesium type. They are dark rocks, and are generally heavier than rocks of the sial. The islands that jut up from the deep Pacific Basin are volcanic islands of the sima type.

A zone of glassy rock is believed to be just beneath the sima at the upper

In 1960, earthquakes and volcanic eruptions spread destruction and disaster over large areas in Chile, a country whose volcanoes are part of the "ring of fire" around the Pacific Ocean basin.

edge of the mantle. This glassy rock melts easily under the great heat and pressure 30 to 40 miles down inside the earth. The presence of this rock zone may account for movements below the crust of the earth and for the shifting of rock as mountains are formed and as ocean basins settle.

The melted magma which forms igneous rock seems to have its beginning at least 20 or 30 miles down, and perhaps as much as 100 to 500 miles down. Somewhere in this zone the temperature is high enough to melt rock, while at the same time, the pressure is so high that the rock transmits earthquake waves and acts like a solid.

Earth movements relieving strains and pressures in the crust create zones of weakness or actual breaks. These permit some of the magma to find its way up into the crust either through cracks

Below, *a cutaway diagram of a volcano.*

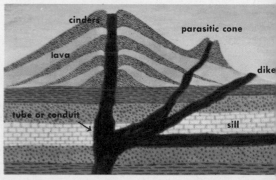

26

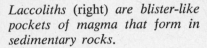

Dikes (left) *are sheet-like intrusions formed by hot magma that follows cracks and joints in rock structures below the surface.*

Laccoliths (right) *are blister-like pockets of magma that form in sedimentary rocks.*

or by dissolving the weakened rock around it. Sometimes magma moves to the surface, spewing out of volcanoes or spreading over the countryside in huge lava flows. Lava is only one type of igneous rock, but it is probably the best known. Most magma cools well below the surface of the earth. Under these conditions it cools very slowly.

Inside the crust of the earth, magma may flow into branching cracks forming veins. It may cut across layers of rock forming great sheet-like dikes. When magma flows between layers it forces the rock apart. Such an intrusion is known as a sill. Sills may be anywhere from a few inches to hundreds of feet in thickness.

Sometimes intrusive rock, forced between layers, will raise the upper layers like a blister. Such blisters a few miles or so across are called laccoliths. Many are found in the western part of the United States. Larger intrusive blisters may cover thousands of square miles. These are batholiths, which form large parts of the Rocky Mountains and northern Canada.

Sills form when magma flows more or less evenly between layers of sedimentary rock. Shown below are The Palisades along the Hudson River.

Sometimes during cooling, basalt sills crack into many 5-sided columns. One of the best-known of such sills, exposed by erosion, is Giant's Causeway in Ireland.

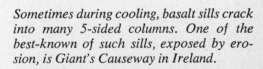

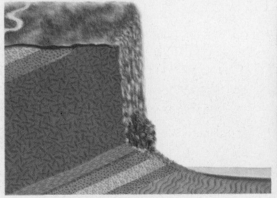

GRANITE

PEGMATITE

PORPHYRY

SYENITE

Intrusive rocks are formed below the earth's surface as the hot magma cools.

DIORITE

GABBRO

PERIDOTITE

Magma that intrudes or pushes into other rock cools beneath the surface of the earth and hence cools more slowly. Minerals separate out and crystals develop. Shrinkage may split the cooling rock into huge regular columns. Millions of years later the rocks above may be worn down and the igneous rocks are exposed at the surface. Then these hidden structures can be studied and the valuable minerals in or near them can be mined.

When magma does reach the earth's surface it cools much more rapidly. The rock it forms is then called an *extrusive rock* because it is pushed out onto the surface. The cooling of extrusive rock may be so fast that the magma does not form minerals at all, but a kind of natural glass or obsidian. This natural glass, usually dark brown or black, is almost exactly the same as the glass used in making windows or bottles. Indians prized it for arrows and

Volcanoes and lava flows are the most typical of extrusive rocks.

1 cinder cone
2 spatter cone
3 shield lava cone
4 compound volcano
5 radiating dike
6 lava flow

spearheads. It is sometimes used for simple jewelry.

Magma may contain a great deal of gas. As it reaches the surface this gas escapes, causing the magma to bubble and froth as the rock cools. When there are so many gas bubbles that the natural glass is whipped into a froth, the rock is called pumice—a rock usually light in color and so light in weight that it will float on water. When the gas bubbles are larger, the volcanic rock looks like coarse cinders. Dark, heavy basalt is one of the most abundant lavas, but there are also light colored lavas rich in silica. Some lavas, thrown high in the air, cool as they fall, forming rounded or twisted volcanic bombs.

Igneous rocks are important to us because of the rich mineral deposits in them or in veins which are found in them. From such veins we get most of our gold, lead, zinc, mercury, arsenic, antimony, nickel, cobalt and titanium. The value of these mineral deposits runs into billions of dollars.

Igneous rocks were the first kind of rocks to form. Some are known to be over two billion years old. At the same time, some other igneous rocks are the youngest rocks, for there are active volcanoes still spewing lava from their craters this very day. Igneous rocks, more than any other kind, offer proof that the earth is still growing, changing and constantly rebuilding its mountains and hillsides.

OBSIDIAN

RHYOLITE

PUMICE

ANDESITE

BASALT

SCORIA

AMYGDALOIDAL BASALT

29

Glaciers

Gravity

Plants

River

Sedimentary Rocks

The second and perhaps most familiar group of rocks is made of nothing more than debris, waste and rubble. The geologist speaks of most of them as fragmental or clastic rocks—those formed from fragments or debris of other rocks. Clastic rocks cannot be the oldest, for by their very definition they have been formed from other rocks. Yet in many ways they are more interesting than any of the earliest rocks. Nobody knows what the surface of the earth was like when it was first formed. But if in those primeval times, rocks were broken up, weathered and washed away, the forces of nature such as we know them today must also have been present long ago.

Sedimentary rocks provide us with evidence that for at least a billion years —and perhaps more—conditions on the earth's surface were very much as they are today. An atmosphere contained the sun's heat. Rain, wind, running water, and the chemicals of the air changed the surface rocks. This process of weathering and erosion began as soon as the first rocks formed, and it continues today. In colder regions, snow changes to ice and ice forms glaciers, which move slowly over the land, wearing down the rocks and carrying fragments away. In past ages, great ice sheets spread over much of North America, Europe, even covering parts of the African continent.

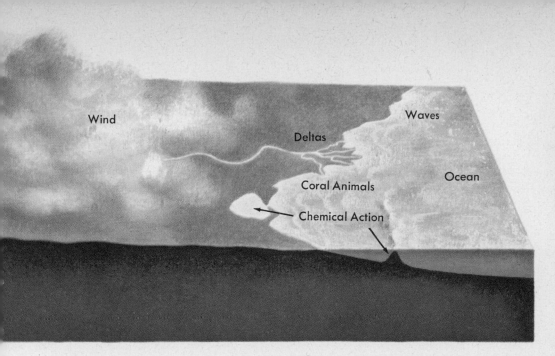

Wind

Deltas

Waves

Coral Animals

Ocean

Chemical Action

Sedimentary rocks are made up of particles or fragments of older rocks. They have in common only the fact that they have somehow been moved from their original place. They vary widely in texture, composition, and color, and are formed by the action of erosion by wind, water, or ice, or gravity or chemical action.

Even raindrops that fall help wear away the rocks. But the water that runs over the land or through the cracks in the rocks wears them even more. The heat of the sun splits rocks open. Frosts of winter splinter them, too. Plant roots, growing into cracks, swell and push the rocks apart. All these kinds of actions break the rocks into smaller and smaller fragments which are finally carried away by gravity, water and even by the wind.

Sooner or later these fragments move down to lower and lower levels because of the action of gravity. Rivers drop sand and mud in deltas at the shore of the sea. Lakes are gradually filled with washed-in sediment; so are the dry desert basins. Wherever sand, mud, silt and dust are deposited, they slowly become cemented together, forming sedimentary rock.

Tree roots and roots of smaller plants help split rocks apart.

31

Erosion of sedimentary layers often leaves towers, buttes, and mesas.

Sedimentary rocks form in different ways in many places. But the rocks are always made up of particles or fragments from older rocks. Sometimes the fragments are stones and boulders, sometimes pebbles, sometimes fine sand or finer clay. Chemical action in shallow seas and in hot springs may form deposits of even finer chemical sediments. Sedimentary rocks make up about 75 per cent of the exposed land surface of the earth. But they make up less than 5 per cent of the total volume of the earth's crust.

Sedimentary rocks are often classified according to the way they have formed and according to the size of the particles in them. Following this classification, we begin with fragments which were broken or worn from older rocks. When such fragments are pebbles or larger, they become cemented together to form a rock called conglomerate. If the fragments are sharp and angular, showing that they have not been transported far, the conglomerate is called a breccia. If the fragments are

worn, rounded, and show scratches from glacial ice, the conglomerate is called a tillite.

When the rock fragments are smaller, like individual grains of sand (roughly .0025 inch to .25 inch in diameter), the rock is called a sandstone. Sandstones may be fine or coarse, hard or soft. Usually they are composed of grains of sand or silica. Sometimes other minerals are present and then the sandstone is given a special name. Arkose, for example, is a sandstone formed under desert conditions. It contains grains of feldspar as well as grains of quartz. Sandstones form about 32 per cent of all sedimentary rock.

When the rock particles are still smaller in size, so small that they are difficult to see, the rock is a shale. Shales tend to be rich in clay minerals, though they may contain large amounts of silica. Shales are usually fine-grained, light or dark in color, and they often break in a typical way. Shales are the most common of sedimentary

CONGLOMERATE

RAINDROPS ON SHALE

FINE
SANDSTONE

ARKOSE

CALCAREOUS SHALE

COARSE
SANDSTONE

OÖLITIC LIMESTONE

SANDY SHALE

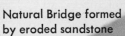

Natural Bridge formed
by eroded sandstone

CRYSTALLINE LIMESTONE

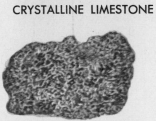

TUFA

SHELL LIMESTONE

rocks, forming about 46 per cent of all sedimentary rocks known.

Limestone is a sedimentary rock which does not easily fit in with the others. Limestone has many origins. In some cases it is a clastic rock made of fragments of shells piled on beaches and cemented together by the lime itself. Coquina is coarse limestone made of shell fragments. Of the sedimentary rocks, 22 per cent are limestones.

When clastic fragments are first de-posited, nothing holds them together. They may remain in this state for hundreds of thousands of years. Big piles of sand and gravel were deposited 25,000 or more years ago during the great ice age. In only a few places have these begun to cement together.

Rock fragments will cement together faster when water circulates through them, especially if the water contains dissolved chemicals. Lime is such a chemical. Iron rust is another. It gives

Stalactites and stalagmites are formed in limestone caves where acid waters trickle.

BITUMINOUS COAL

LIGNITE COAL

ANTHRACITE COAL

Three kinds of coal are formed from certain decayed plants.
Each kind is identified by the amount of "fixed carbon" in it.

sandstone and shale a yellowish or reddish color. Silica is a third cement, and when sandstones are cemented by silica they are likely to be hard and tough.

A second group of sedimentary rocks includes those of chemical origin. In shallow seas, lakes, and caves, and under certain special conditions, lime is deposited chemically. One form is oölitic limestone, formed of small, round grains about the size of grains of sand. Acid-bearing water trickling through limestone dissolves some of it. The limestone is redeposited as the water evaporates in cracks or caves. Such drippings form stalactites and stalagmites. Dolomite, a magnesium limestone, halite (or salt) and gypsum may also be deposited chemically. All may form beds that are large enough to be classified as sedimentary rock. Great salt beds lie beneath the city of Detroit, Michigan.

Finally, plants and animals produce a few sedimentary rocks. Coal deposits begin as peat, a soft organic material that forms from decaying ferns and swamp plants. As this material is buried by layers of sand and debris, water in the peat is squeezed out and gases are liberated. The amount of carbon gradually increases as the material changes from peat to lignite, a brown coal, and from the brown coal to soft,

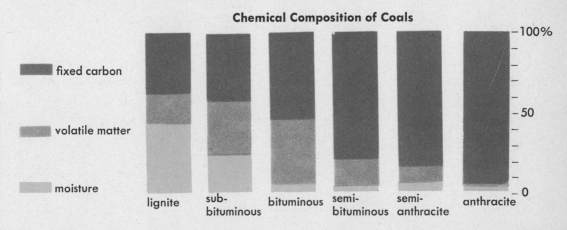

Chemical Composition of Coals

fixed carbon

volatile matter

moisture

lignite — sub-bituminous — bituminous — semi-bituminous — semi-anthracite — anthracite

35

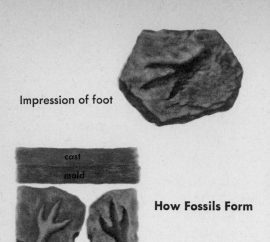

Impression of foot

cast
mold

How Fossils Form

cast   mold

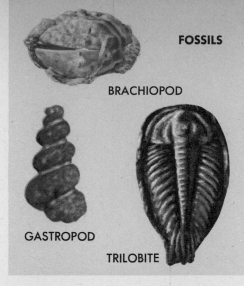

FOSSILS

BRACHIOPOD

GASTROPOD

TRILOBITE

FOSSILS

CARBONIZED FERN LEAF

SHELL FOSSILS

black coal. At each step, as the amount of carbon increases, the amount of hydrogen and oxygen in the material decreases. Coral and similar animals form deposits of organic lime in reefs.

Sometimes sedimentary rocks give a clue to the kinds of life and conditions which existed millions of years ago when the rocks were formed. Fossils are the remains or evidences of life buried in the rock. Sometimes the actual remains are buried; sometimes fossils are impressions, molds or casts. In nearly every case fossils are formed in sedimentary rock, when plants and animals have been buried under debris.

Tough parts of plants and hard parts of animals produce the best fossils. Shells, bones, teeth, leaves, wood and bark are often preserved. Fossils tell the history of the earth and the development of life. In the oldest rock, only the simplest kinds of plants and animals are found. In more recent rocks the plants and animals are different and

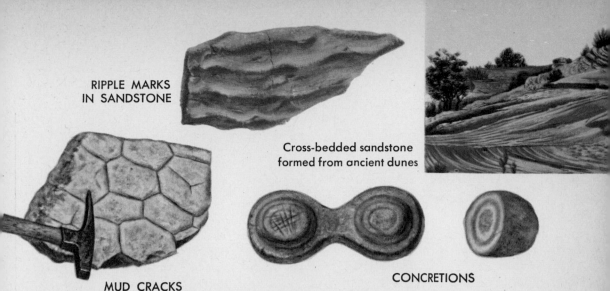

RIPPLE MARKS
IN SANDSTONE

Cross-bedded sandstone
formed from ancient dunes

MUD CRACKS

CONCRETIONS

more complex, showing a great range of adaptations to many environments. It is mainly through the study of fossils that scientists have come to understand how the plant and animal life of today came to be.

Sedimentary rocks, especially those formed in shallow waters, contain ripple marks, formed by the action of waves stirring the bottom. Mud cracks mark the places where the shallow waters dried out, exposing the cracked mud. Later the cracks were filled with soft mud, preserving their pattern.

The layers of sedimentary rock often form parallel beds. A storm may wash down coarse material. During the winter when a lake is covered with ice, only the finest material is deposited. Sometimes the beds are tilted where a stream is depositing sand and mud at its mouth. All these features are preserved in sedimentary rocks and help to show how they were formed.

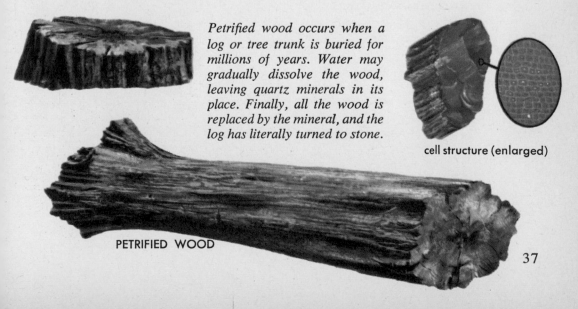

Petrified wood occurs when a log or tree trunk is buried for millions of years. Water may gradually dissolve the wood, leaving quartz minerals in its place. Finally, all the wood is replaced by the mineral, and the log has literally turned to stone.

cell structure (enlarged)

PETRIFIED WOOD

37

The Grand Tetons in Wyoming have been carved by glaciers and running water.

Metamorphic Rocks

If anything is characteristic of the world of rocks, it is change. The slow actions of running water will, through millions of years, carve a Grand Canyon. Mountains are worn away and ocean basins are slowly filled over long periods of time. Changes that affect the features of the earth affect the rocks also. Rocks which have been changed so that their characters are altered are known as metamorphic rocks.

All rocks change after they are formed. The atmosphere, circulating water, the pressure of overlying rocks —all have some effect. But when these processes continue for a long time, or when they cause marked changes in the rock, then metamorphic rocks are formed. Some metamorphic rocks have been changed so much that they are completely different from the rocks from which they were formed. Unless these rocks are studied carefully, geologists cannot be sure of their origin.

Many forces in the crust of the earth change rocks. The most important of these forces are heat and pressure. Often the two forces are related, as when movements in the crust of the earth exert pressure which produces heat. Often heat comes from intruded magma. Magma at a temperature of 2,000 degrees or more may find its way into the overlying rock. The heat of the magma bakes and alters the nearby rock. If the mass of magma is large, the rate of cooling is slow. Then the effect of heat may be pronounced.

Metamorphic or "changed" rocks occur as a result of heat, pressure, or penetration by other substances. The deeper under the surface a rock is, the greater is the heat and pressure on it. Shifts in the earth's crust, or volcanic activity may cause changes in the mineral content of such rocks. Water, gases or fluids may permeate them causing other changes.

When hot intruded rocks alter the rock on either side, the effect is described as contact metamorphism. The adjoining rocks are baked. Their mineral content may be changed, but the changes are usually limited to a narrow border zone, a few inches or a few feet.

Metamorphism is not only due to hot rocks, but to hot gases and hot liquids which flow from them. The hot gases move up through cracks to make closer contact with nearby rocks and minerals. These volatile deposits may produce many new minerals. Hot solutions do the same thing and are likely to transport even more new minerals than hot gases. Heated waters have a much lower temperature than magma and bring their own kinds of minerals with them. The zeolites and arsenic minerals are examples of low-temperature deposits.

The effect of heat and hot chemical solutions is sometimes called local metamorphism in contrast to regional metamorphism, which affects large areas. Regional metamorphism usually involves movements within the crust of the earth. The origins of these movements are hard to explain. They are

The diagram at left shows how mountains are formed by folding and thrust-faulting, as huge masses of rock are pushed horizontally.

Mountains are formed by block-faulting where underground movements raise and tilt huge blocks of rock.

The Appalachians are folded mountains with deep parallel valleys.

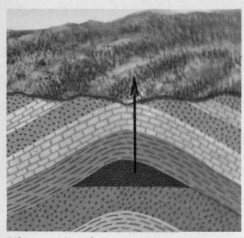

Oil or gas may be trapped in pockets made by upward thrusts called anticlines.

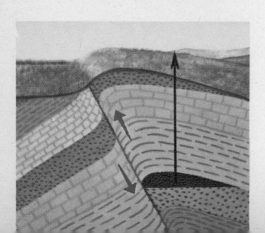

probably related to a shifting in the earth's crust as rocks and minerals are moved from one part of the earth to another by erosion. Regional metamorphism can raise or lower the level of rocks. Rocks may be tilted, folded, stretched or broken. Great masses of rock may be pushed over one another, forming zones of crushed rock. Sometimes these actions are slow and gentle, taking place over many thousands of years. Then very little change in the rock takes place.

At other times metamorphism is more rugged and the rocks are altered very much. Layers of soft coal are transformed into anthracite. Folding

Faults, caused by a shifting in the earth's crust, are a break in rock strata that cause a section of rock to become dislocated along the line of fracture.

40

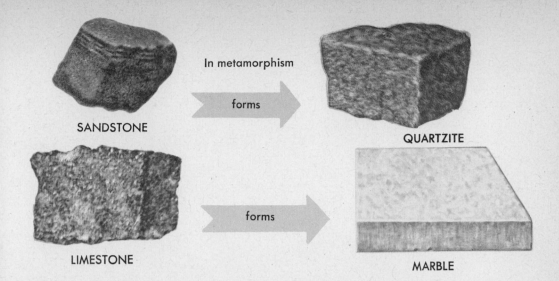

SANDSTONE

In metamorphism

forms →

QUARTZITE

LIMESTONE

forms →

MARBLE

and squeezing these layers of coal removes most of the remaining gases and squeezes out any traces of water. This increases the percentage of carbon in the coal. Similar movements apply pressure to oils in shale or sand, and form traps where the oil and natural gas may be concentrated.

Metamorphic rocks are hard to describe and harder to classify. Their appearance depends on the kind and the degree of change. One example of metamorphism is the alteration of soft sandstones to quartzite. This is a hard, tough, metamorphic rock—so tough that it breaks through the grains of sand as well as through the cement. Quartzite is harder, tougher, and more durable than the sandstone from which it was made.

SHALE

forms →

SLATE

and may be further metamorphosed into

PHYLLITE

and →

MICA SCHIST

41

Marble, a metamorphosed limestone, is popular as building material both for its strength and beauty. This is the Lincoln Memorial in Washington, D. C.

Limestones are affected by heat, pressure, and circulating liquids to produce marble, a metamorphic rock. Some limestones are only slightly metamorphosed and the changes in them are difficult to see. Crystals and fossils in the rock are not altered much, if at all. While some of these slightly altered limestones are beautiful, they are not true marble. A more thorough metamorphism is needed.

Shale, formed from mud and silt, becomes metamorphosed into slate. Shale itself tends to break in flat layers. This is even more true of slate. However, slate breaks along lines that are usually at an angle to the original beds of the shale. Since slate splits so easily, it was once widely used for shingles, blackboards and paving. If the pressure that forms slate continues to act, a chemical reaction sets in, causing mica crystals to form. This new rock is called phyllite. It is a fine-grained

Some marbles are slightly altered; others are true metamorphic rocks.

BROWN MARBLE

BLACK MARBLE

One possible alteration of a
sedimentary rock into granite

SHALE

GRANITE

SCHIST

GNEISS

slate, glittering with almost micro-scopic flecks of mica. If the process continues further, the grains of mica grow larger and the result is a rock that is called schist.

All kinds of rock can be metamor-phosed — even metamorphic rocks. Some volcanic rocks have been changed into schists. Quartz sandstone may be metamorphosed into quartzite, and in turn this may be altered into a quartz schist. Finally, granite, an igne-ous or metamorphic rock, may be changed into gneiss, a coarse rock which contains a good deal of mica. Hence, gneiss is not as strong a rock as the granite from which it was made. Other kinds of rock may be altered into gneiss, too.

Some of the changes in the crust of the earth and in the rocks have been so complex that geologists are not sure just what has happened. Granite, for example, is sometimes an igneous rock,

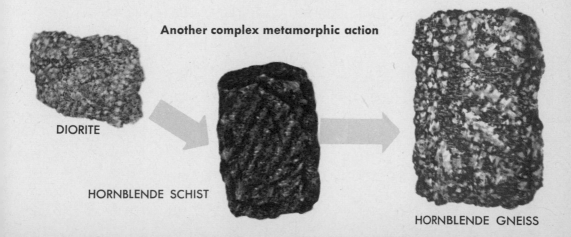

Another complex metamorphic action

DIORITE

HORNBLENDE SCHIST

HORNBLENDE GNEISS

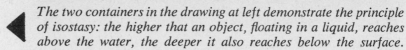

The two containers in the drawing at left demonstrate the principle of isostasy: the higher that an object, floating in a liquid, reaches above the water, the deeper it also reaches below the surface.

Geologists apply the theory of isostasy to the rock structures in the crust of the earth: granite rock masses "float" in basalt, which is heavier, and the higher the mountains, the further they penetrate below the earth's level into the basalt below.

coming from a magma rich in silica and aluminum. It may also be a type of metamorphic rock so altered by invading materials that there is little or no trace of what the original rock might have been. It is possible to find a whole series of rocks grading from normal sedimentary kinds through schists and gneisses, which show an increasing amount of mica and feldspar, into crystalline rocks which clearly look like granite.

The changes in the crust of the earth producing the different kinds of rocks are all part of a great cycle in which mountains are built up and mountains are worn down; in which the land is raised and the land is lowered. As mountains are worn down over periods of millions of years, the debris finds its way into the ocean basins, increasing their weight, while the weight of the continent is lightened. This puts a strain on the crust of the earth. The strain adjusts itself by means of movements which cause earthquakes and which, over long periods of time, elevate new mountains. Volcanoes form a great circle around the deep Pacific Basin. (p. 25). This "ring of fire" is in itself an indication of a kind of strain or weakness. Lavas pour forth as part of the readjustment.

These earth movements are on such a large scale and involve such long periods of time that it is difficult to observe them first hand. It is not likely that continents have been lost in the Atlantic or that large islands have suddenly appeared. Most of the continents have occupied the same relative positions in the crust of the earth for millions of years. During some eras, shallow seas invaded the continents and sedimentary rocks were deposited, as in the great Mississippi Basin. But sooner or later the continents emerged and have continued to be areas of uplift. At other times the continental shelf (the shallow ocean bottom surrounding the continents), now submerged, has been raised, and the continents were much larger than at present. At one period Alaska and Siberia formed a land bridge between Asia and America, and Australia joined Southern Asia.

During Cretaceous time, over 100 million years ago, a land bridge connected Alaska and Siberia and shallow seas covered much of North America.

45

Soil, the most common surface rock, appears in many different forms. Residual soils (left), *are formed by the gradual decay of surface rock. Tropical soils* (right), *are formed by the action of heavy rains and warm air. Transported soil* (below left), *develops from parent soil that has been moved by ice, wind or water. Northern forest soils* (below right), *form under the acid materials deposited by pine forests.*

Rocks In Our Lives

In the year 2000 when men have reached the moon and when space travel is an everyday occurrence, people will still be depending on the rocks in the earth. This has been true for a million years and will probably be true for another million, if the human race survives. If the human race does not survive, it may well be that our use and misuse of the rocks in the crust of the earth will have brought about our extinction. This could happen through men's depleting the soil, exhausting the natural fuels, or destroying plants, animals and human life through radioactive fallout coming indirectly from uranium and other radioactive ores.

Today rocks are so important to us that they are used nearly everywhere. The weathered rock, mixed with the remains of dead plants, becomes the soil, on which we depend for crops, forests, and grasslands. Some rock minerals turn into soluble form through weather-

PITCHBLENDE

CARNOTITE

ing. Plants must have these minerals for normal growth. The fertilizers we add to the soil come mainly from rocks and from the atmosphere.

The fuels we use today come from rocks also. Coal, oil and natural gas are found in sedimentary rocks. Atomic fuels come from the rocks, also. But the supply of uranium and thorium is not very great and will not last forever.

We are equally dependent on the rocks for all the metals which are the backbone of most industries. Some iron ores occur in igneous and metamorphic rocks, but most are found in sandstones and shales where they have probably been concentrated by the action of bacteria. Aluminum is fast replacing iron for some uses. It is even more common than iron in the crust of the earth. But

MANUFACTURE OF ALUMINUM

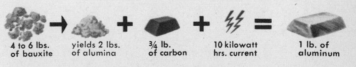

4 to 6 lbs. of bauxite — yields 2 lbs. of alumina + ¾ lb. of carbon + 10 kilowatt hrs. current = 1 lb. of aluminum

BAUXITE

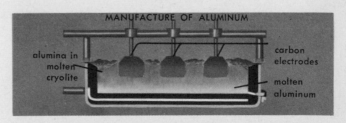

MANUFACTURE OF ALUMINUM

alumina in molten cryolite

carbon electrodes

molten aluminum

Aluminum, even more abundant in the earth than iron, is yielded chiefly from the ore, bauxite. It has been known as a commercial metal for over a century, and now about a million tons are used every year.

ORES OF OTHER METALS

WOLFRAMITE
(Tungsten)

SCHEELITE
(Tungsten)

MOLYBDENITE
(Molybdenum)

COBALTITE
(Cobalt)

NICCOLITE
(Nickel)

CHROMITE
(Chromium)

ILMENITE
(Titanium)

ILMENITE
CRYSTAL

aluminum ores are difficult to find. A cheap way of getting aluminum from clay may be the great discovery of the next decade. Copper, lead, tin, zinc, gold, silver, and other metals all come from ores found in rock. These ores are usually found with igneous rocks and may be carried by the liquids and vapors that escape from magmas into nearby cracks and fissures.

Some of the lesser known metals are of great importance. They make possible a wide range of steel alloys which can do jobs impossible with carbon steel. The ores of most of these metals are quite rare and only limited deposits of commercial grade have been found. Most are associated with igneous rocks formed deep in the earth's crust which has been exposed by ages of weathering and erosion.

Tungsten gives us the filaments of electric lights. Combined with carbon it makes a compound so hard that it is excelled only by diamonds as an industrial cutting tool. One to three per cent tungsten in steel makes the steel unusually hard. Tungsten steel tools will retain a cutting edge at even red heat. Molybdenum added to steel gives a similar effect, and it is widely used in making tool steels. Molybdenite, the most important ore, is found in southwest areas marked by volcanic activity and especially in the state of Colorado.

Many of the lesser known metals have found wide commercial use.

48

Cobalt, related to nickel, occurs with it in the deposits at Ontario, Canada. Cobalt is magnetic, and its alloys are used in making magnet iron. Small amounts of cobalt give glass a beautiful deep blue color. Nickel is more common than cobalt and has many more uses, especially in steel alloys that resist heat and corrosion. Stainless steels contain nickel and chromium. Nickel is also used in coins and in many chemical processes.

Chromium, too, is used in many steel alloys and also with nickel in plating steel. The bright finish on automobiles makes chromium a familiar metal. Cuba, Turkey, and Brazil have large ore deposits. Titanium minerals are fairly common but uses for the hard metal are still new. It is finding an important place in rockets and other high-temperature engines.

Another group of metals which show great promise for future use are the very light ores. Aluminum is best known but magnesium, which weighs only 65% as much, has new uses in airplane and other construction. The ores are common but the amount of magnesium in the sea is enormous—a cubic mile of ocean water contains 12 million pounds of this light metal.

Lithium, the lightest of all metals, is light enough to float easily. It has many chemical uses. New possibilities in al-

Some beryllium minerals are better known as the gems, emerald and aquamarine.

49

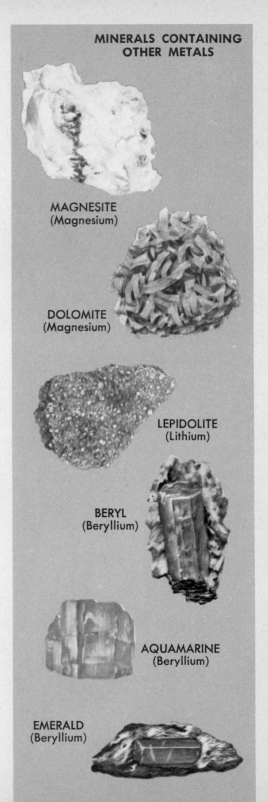

MINERALS CONTAINING OTHER METALS

MAGNESITE
(Magnesium)

DOLOMITE
(Magnesium)

LEPIDOLITE
(Lithium)

BERYL
(Beryllium)

AQUAMARINE
(Beryllium)

EMERALD
(Beryllium)

COARSE GABBRO

CRAB ORCHARD STONE

RED GRANITE

loys are turning up as a result of constant experimenting. Lepidolite is a lithium mica, but most of the metal is obtained from chemicals in salt brines.

Beryllium is a good deal lighter than aluminum but is too rare to have possibilities as a metal. Fortunately, small amounts blended with copper and other metals make important alloys. Some beryllium minerals are transparent and of gem quality. Best known are emer-

alds, aquamarines and morganite. Synthetic emeralds now duplicate the beauty of the natural gems.

Rocks are widely used in building, both for their strength and for their beauty. Many large buildings and monuments are built of granite and marble. Sandstones and limestones are quarried for building purposes, too. Most important of all are mixtures of shale which are crushed, combined

MANUFACTURE OF CEMENT

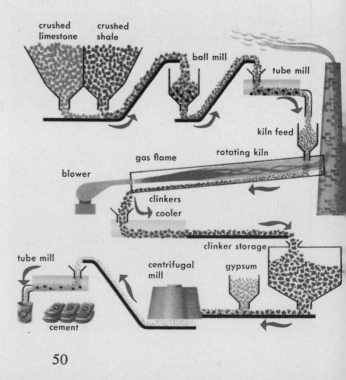

crushed limestone | crushed shale | ball mill | tube mill | kiln feed | gas flame | rotating kiln | blower | clinkers | cooler | clinker storage | tube mill | centrifugal mill | gypsum | cement

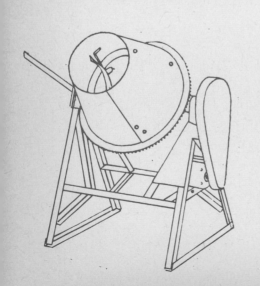

50

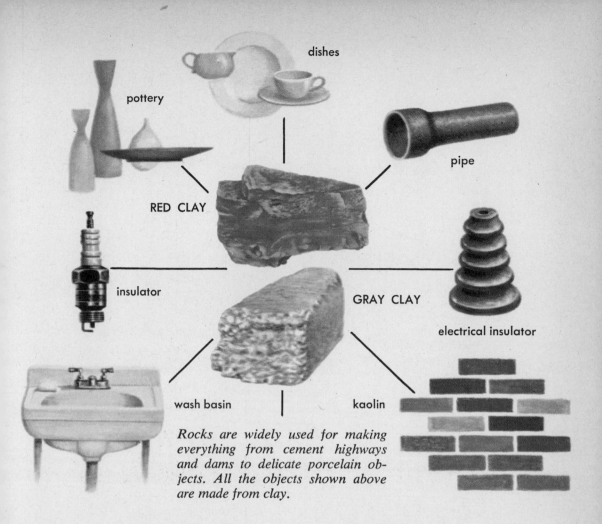

pottery

dishes

pipe

RED CLAY

insulator

GRAY CLAY

electrical insulator

wash basin

kaolin

Rocks are widely used for making everything from cement highways and dams to delicate porcelain objects. All the objects shown above are made from clay.

with slag and lime, then heated to about 2,600 degrees in giant kilns. Gypsum is added. The clinker is ground to a fine powder—cement. Cement, when mixed with sand and water, sets to become a hard solid. Crushed rock is added to the mixture to make concrete, which can be poured to make roads, dams or buildings.

Bricks are made from clay, but in modern buildings concrete blocks are often used. Clay is now used for tile,

Kaolin is used in making fine ceramics.

drains and pipe. Finer clay or kaolin is used for expensive ceramics, power line insulators, dishes, and bathroom and kitchen fixtures. Kitchen pots and the

KAOLIN

51

Glass, made from sand, lime and soda, has become one of the most important products man has developed from rocks. Here, a delicate hand operation is carried out in a modern glass factory. Machinery is now used in making most commercial glassware.

iron of the kitchen stove may be covered with enamel or porcelain, made mainly from feldspars. This glasslike covering protects the metal and makes it easy to clean.

Another important product from rock is glass. Discovered by accident over 2,000 years ago, glass did not become widely used until the 16th century. Now there are hundreds of kinds of glass for as many different uses. Sand or silica is the most important ingredi-

ent. Lime and soda are added, and lead oxide makes the mixture melt more easily. Chemicals containing copper, gold, cobalt, manganese and uranium give glass a variety of colors. The manufacture of glass is done at very high temperatures, using great furnaces kept at about 2,000 degrees. Each may hold nearly 2,000 tons of molten material. As glass is removed, fresh raw material is added so the process is a continuous one.

52

SAPPHIRE

DIAMOND IN MATRIX

RUBY

Much of the working of glass is done automatically. Huge machines make thousands of bottles an hour, and even more ingenious machines manufacture electric light bulbs at a rate of nearly half a million a day.

These are only a few samples of the importance of rocks and the minerals they contain in our daily lives. In addition to the many uses that make agriculture, industry and commerce possible, rocks are prized for their beauty. Many are used as ornamental and building stones and in others are rare deposits of those special minerals we call gems, minerals which we value for their beauty and rarity.

The real beauty of rocks is in the variety they give to the surface of the earth. Rocks create the majestic peaks of the Rockies, the Alps and the Himalayas. They make the loneliness of the Sahara and the grandeur of the Grand Canyon. The great volcanoes are beautiful and fearful. In this modern age we may be looking toward space, but our roots are still deep in the rocks which make up the earth.

Index

Picture Credits: p. 11, Courtesy U.S. Navy; p. 12 (top), F. H. Pough, American Museum of Natural History; p. 12 (bot.), Union Pacific Railroad; p. 13 (top), British Information Service; p. 31 (bot.), p. 38, p. 40 (top), C. J. Schuberth, American Museum of Natural History; p. 34, Marion Smak; p. 52, Corning Glass Works; p. 53 (bot.), Bruce Hunter, American Museum of Natural History.